Project White Shark:
The Monterey Bay
Aquarium's Quest
to Understand
and Exhibit the
Great White Shark

In the pre-dawn hours

on a Thursday in March 2005, two small boats headed out into Monterey Bay carrying precious cargo: the first great white shark ever successfully kept at an aquarium. After six-and-a-half months on exhibit at the Monterey Bay Aquarium, she was going home.

The young shark thrived

during her time at the aquarium, and attracted legions of fans for a species more often demonized than adored. Her journey had begun four years earlier, when the aquarium launched its white shark research project with two ambitious goals: To learn more about the lives of great white sharks in the wild; and to become the first aquarium ever to exhibit, and release, a young great white.

The aquarium team releases
a great white shark in
Monterey Bay.

Now, lying calmly in a stretcher with seawater flowing over her gills, she was fitted with an electronic tracking tag. The white shark team angled the stretcher toward the water and spread one end wide. The shark glided free. She circled the boats once, twice – her distinctive dorsal fin cutting a sharp line as she turned. Then she slipped below the surface and

disappeared into the wild.

How It All Began

Fear and fascination define the human relationship with the great white shark. It's a top predator in the ocean, a place we visit but where we're never truly at home. It strikes without warning, then vanishes as suddenly as it appeared.

Though people are never the intended target, and rarely the inadvertent victim, shark attacks are headline news. Peter Benchley cemented the iconic status of great white sharks in the public imagination with his best-seller, *Jaws*, and the blockbuster summer movie that followed.

"If there's one thing I'm dead certain of," Benchley said years later, "it's that I could not write *Jaws* today. I could not turn this beautiful beast into a villain."

Despite their powerful presence in the human imagination, great white sharks remain creatures of mystery. We know little about their lives, including where and how they live, and where their young are born. For all their strengths, they're a threatened species – just like the charismatic predators on land: tigers, lions and wolves. They're identified internationally as vulnerable to extinction, and protected in many parts of the world.

For half a century, public aquariums dreamed of putting visitors face to face with a great white. A few tried, and no shark survived longer than 16 days. Many thought it was impossible. Others deemed it the "Holy Grail" of exhibit animals.

Against that background, the Monterey Bay Aquarium stepped forward to do two things: Learn more about their lives through a strong research program, and – for the first time – keep a great white shark on exhibit for an extended time.

"We don't just fear our predators. We're trans-fixed by them, prone to weave stories and fables and to chatter endlessly about them... In a deeply tribal sense, we love our monsters."

E.O. Wilson

Steps To Success

To succeed where others had failed, the aquarium team committed itself to a new process that gave equal weight to research into the lives of great white sharks in the wild, and efforts to place a young shark on exhibit. The White Shark Research Project was born in 2002, but its roots were much deeper.

Over a long career, David Powell, the aquarium's first husbandry director, was involved in several efforts to exhibit great white sharks. He championed construction of a million-gallon Open Sea exhibit that was designed with the needs of pelagic fishes in mind. Tunas and sharks did well when the exhibit opened in 1996. The aquarium team now had an exhibit that it believed could one day meet the needs of a great white shark.

Powell also realized there were flaws in the typical path aquariums followed in trying to exhibit a great white. Generally, they'd get a call from a fisherman who'd accidentally caught a great white and who offered to bring the animal in for exhibit. The shark would arrive, its health condition unknown, and then would go straight into an exhibit that wasn't designed with open-water sharks in mind.

Powell suggested a new approach – a halfway house where the sharks could acclimate for a time. Led by Vice President of Husbandry Randy Hamilton, the aquarium's team had already developed and tested a way to move sharks from southern California to Monterey – especially great white sharks that must swim constantly to force oxygen-rich water over their gills. They'd created a "tunabago" – a mobile life-support vessel, like a space capsule for ocean animals – that proved its mettle in the long-distance transport of tunas and other open-ocean animals.

Powell was one of several white shark experts assembled by the aquarium early in 2002 to identify the steps they thought essential to keeping a great white on exhibit. With their advice in hand, the aquarium committed $1.1 million to a three-year program of field studies and attempts to collect and transport a young great white shark to Monterey.

The guiding philosophy, said John O'Sullivan, curator of field operations and de facto leader of the white shark team, was "slow, methodical and systematic."

The plan looked good on paper. Would it work in the field?

SIZE: 13 FT. X 7 FT. X 7.5 FT. / CAPACITY: 3,200 GA

LIFE SUPPORT: CIRCULATED, FILTERED WATER WITH OX

The tunabago.

The aquarium's Husbandry team had already
developed a way to move sharks. They'd created
a "tunabago" – a mobile life-support vessel, like
a space capsule for ocean animals – that proved
its mettle in the long-distance transport of tunas
and other open-ocean animals.

The First Years

n May 2002, the team took to the field. They'd laid the groundwork by partnering with research colleagues and commercial fishermen in southern California, where young great whites appear seasonally in this nursery area. (There's speculation that mother sharks give birth in southern California waters, though no one has ever observed the birth of a great white shark.)

Fishermen agreed to let the scientists tag and release young sharks caught accidentally in nets they set to catch halibut and seabass. Their cooperation generated vital information about how well the sharks survived the stress of capture. The answer, it turns out, is much better than the aquarium team or other scientists predicted.

Electronic tracking tags also generated the first accurate data on the movements of young great whites, basic information essential for fisheries managers charged with protecting sharks in nursery waters that extend from Santa Barbara to Baja California.

The aquarium also partnered with scientists at Stanford University's Hopkins Marine Station to tag and track adult great whites in their winter feeding grounds off the Farallon Islands and Point Año Nuevo, near San Francisco Bay. As with young sharks, little was known about the lives of adult great white sharks, including where they traveled.

In waters off Malibu, the aquarium anchored a four-million-gallon net pen – the halfway house first suggested by Powell. The tunabago sat at the ready, back in Monterey.

Tagged.

Fishermen agreed to let the scientists tag and release young sharks caught accidentally in nets they set to catch halibut and seabass. Their cooperation generated vital information about how well the sharks survived the stress of capture.

In that first season in 2002, the team put zero sharks in the pen and tagged just one shark in the field. It was, as O'Sullivan said, "a learning year." After consulting with researchers and fishermen – some of whom had almost a sixth sense, developed over a lifetime at sea, about when the waters looked "sharky" – they returned to the field in July 2003. Remarkably, in August, one of the partner fishermen caught a shark unintentionally in his net and brought it to the pen. It was a healthy male, swimming strongly, and it made a meal from food hung in the pen. It had all the markers of a successful exhibit candidate, and the team prepared to bring it to Monterey.

But there was a problem.

The pen was a rental, and the owner needed it back for his tuna-ranching operation off Baja California. After five days in the pen, the shark had fed, but it hadn't yet taken three meals, a benchmark that the aquarium's "slow, methodical and systematic" protocol required. Time was running out.

On August 4, the shark was released to the wild and the empty pen towed south to Mexico. Further attempts would have to wait for another year.

A learning year.

In that first season in 2002, the team put zero sharks in the pen and tagged just one shark in the field. It was, as O'Sullivan said, "a learning year."

First Shark in Monterey

Their success in the previous year buoyed the team as it headed out for the third year of the field project. Data from young animals tagged and released in the wild showed that these white sharks naturally spent 75 percent of their time in water temperatures and at depths similar to those in the aquarium's exhibit. It was another indication that the exhibit had real potential.

In 2004, there was no rental deadline. The aquarium owned the pen. And, on August 20, a commercial fisherman brought a young female shark he found entangled in his halibut gillnet off Huntington Beach. Like the male shark in 2003, she navigated the pen well and appeared to be feeding – taking fish from lines lowered into the pen and perhaps feasting on schools of fish swimming inside the net.

Healthy and stable, she was brought to Monterey on September 14 in the 3,200-gallon tunabago. She made her public debut the next morning at 10, then stunned the aquarium husbandry team when she devoured a salmon steak they offered her that same morning.

She was an instant sensation, attracting international media attention and admiring crowds. And she thrived.

One pleasant surprise, O'Sullivan said, was the way she settled into the exhibit.

"We all agreed that after everything we did, developing the methods, time in the field, and research – if she just swam around at the bottom of the tank, we would have failed!" he said. "The fact she was so majestic and swam with a 'swagger' – like the way John Wayne walked – and had such presence in the main window – that was the real reward."

She quickly broke the old record of 16 days for keeping a great white shark at an aquarium, and was on her way to an eventual 198 days on exhibit. A "young of the year" born sometime in the 12 months before she was accidentally caught, she grew from an initial size of 4-feet-7 inches long and a weight of 62 pounds to a length at release of 6-feet-1 inch and a weight of 162 pounds.

On September 15, 2004 she made her public debut. She was an instant sensation, becoming, in the words of Executive Director Julie Packard, "the most powerful emissary for ocean conservation in our history."

The shark changed people's attitudes, too. She became, in the words of Executive Director Julie Packard, "the most powerful emissary for ocean conservation in our history."

The surge in attendance from visitors coming to see her prompted the aquarium's board of trustees to make an additional $500,000 commitment to support field research into the lives of great white sharks.

In March 2005, as she continued to grow in size and popularity, the aquarium followed through on its commitment to return her to the wild when it was in her best interests.

In part because of aggressive interactions with other sharks, in part because her size and weight were making it more of a challenge to move her safely out of the exhibit, the decision was made on March 28. Three days later, on March 31 she slipped back into the Pacific Ocean, carrying an electronic tag programmed to pop free in 30 days. The tag later reported in right on schedule, just north of Santa Barbara. The shark had traveled 200 miles south on a journey that took her more than 100 miles offshore and to depths greater than 800 feet below the surface.

While she awed and inspired visitors, she also taught her caretakers important lessons about white sharks. "We learned a tremendous amount about how to care for these animals," said Associate Curator Manny Ezcurra, who heads the aquarium's white shark exhibit team. "When she arrived, no one even knew if she'd eat, or how long she'd survive. She did so well that we released her after six-and-a-half months because she'd grown so much.

"We found that she had a fantastic capacity to swim in the exhibit, and an impressive ability to heal from injuries. We learned that she preferred to eat salmon over mackerel, and that vitamins we've given to other sharks seem to be effective with a white shark, too. We learned to modify our feeding and handling techniques to keep her healthy, and we observed behavioral changes as she grew."

"From all we've learned," Ezcurra added, "a second shark should do even better than the first."

The release.

On March 31 she slipped back into the Pacific Ocean, carrying an electronic tag programmed to pop free in 30 days.

White Shark Life History

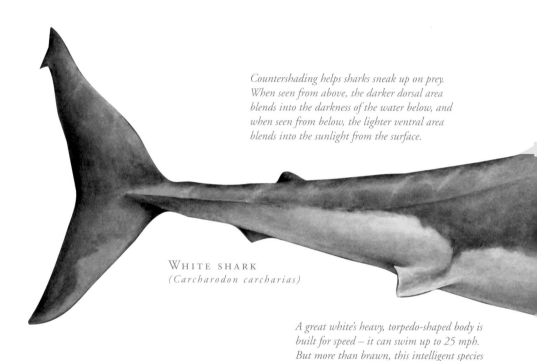

Countershading helps sharks sneak up on prey. When seen from above, the darker dorsal area blends into the darkness of the water below, and when seen from below, the lighter ventral area blends into the sunlight from the surface.

WHITE SHARK
(Carcharodon carcharias)

A great white's heavy, torpedo-shaped body is built for speed – it can swim up to 25 mph. But more than brawn, this intelligent species has a large, well-developed brain that efficiently coordinates its keen senses.

The white shark is a legendary hunter. Dating back 50 million years or more, it's the world's largest predatory fish, and can reach 22 feet in length and weigh more than two tons. It's an apex predator—an animal at the top of the food web, with no natural predators other than humans.

Young white sharks are believed to eat fishes, rays and other sharks. Adults eat larger prey, including pinnipeds (sea lions and seals), fishes, small toothed whales, sea otters and sea turtles. They also eat carrion (dead animals they find floating in the water).

A great white bite is not a haphazard series of chomps, but rather a pre-determined progression. First, white sharks lift their snouts and open their mouths wide enough to fit their food. Then their upper jaws protrude, producing the startling image of exposed upper jaw, teeth and gums. Next, they lift their lower jaws to trap their prey, then finally retract their upper jaws and drop their snouts, applying the force necessary to take a single bite.

Unlike many sharks that have nictitating membranes to protect their eyes, great white sharks do not. Their eyes roll backwards when striking prey.

Adults have up to 300 very sharp teeth, each about three inches long and serrated, like a saw. Narrow teeth on the bottom hold prey; larger triangular ones on top are for cutting.

Because adult white sharks are highly migratory animals found in oceans around the world, little is known about their life history. They may live 20 years or more. They're able to sense minute amounts of blood in the water and the faint electrical fields given off by the bodies of potential prey.

They can swim at speeds up to 25 miles per hour in short bursts, and have been observed leaping out of the water in pursuit of prey. Females give birth to a litter of two to 14 live pups that are up to five feet long. The pups swim away from the mother immediately after birth; there is no maternal care-giving.

Adults can maintain a body temperature 10-18° F above the surrounding water through their large mass and a highly developed heat exchange function in their circulatory system that prevents heat from escaping as blood circulates through the gills and near the body surface. Because warm muscles contract more rapidly than cold ones, an elevated body temperature allows the shark to work efficiently in cold water.

More Sharks, More Success

Since the first shark was released in 2005 after a record 198 days on exhibit, four others (through spring 2011) have spent anywhere from 11 days to four months at the aquarium. Each was tagged and tracked after a successful return to the wild. All demonstrated normal white shark behaviors afterward.

With the confidence the white shark team gained from the first animal, they programmed tracking tags to stay longer and longer on the sharks to learn more about where they traveled after release. Those findings, together with data from 38 young sharks that were tagged and released in the field, provided new and surprising information about the lives of young great white sharks.

The second shark, a somewhat larger candidate for the exhibit, was collected in August 2006 in Santa Monica Bay – not accidentally in commercial fishing gear but intentionally by aquarium staff using hook-and-line gear. It was a new approach, designed to give the team more confidence that the white shark was healthy when he arrived at the ocean pen.

This male added nine inches and 67½ pounds during his 138 days on exhibit before his return to the wild in January 2007. Instead of tracking him for just 30 days after release, his 90-day tracking tag documented a swim from Monterey Bay to the southern tip of Baja California—a journey that took him more than 2,000 miles and to depths of 1,000 feet.

The third shark was caught accidentally in a commercial sea bass net in August 2007 off Ventura. During his 162 days at the aquarium, he added 13 inches and almost 73 pounds. Released in February 2008, he was the first exhibit shark to carry two tracking tags. One stayed with him for 148 days, documenting his migration, as well as the water temperatures and depths he favored. The second was a "Smart Position or Temperature Transmitting (SPOT)" tag that communicated his position, via satellite, each time his dorsal fin broke the surface of the water. From the second tag, the research team learned that he traveled south toward Mazatlán, Mexico in his first 50 days back in the wild. The public was able to track his movements almost in real time on the Tagging of Pacific Predators (TOPP) website.

The fourth shark was collected in August 2008 off southern California, again intentionally by aquarium staff, this time using a purse seine net. She was at the aquarium only for 11 days because, while she was swimming well, she fed just one time during her stay. Unlike her older and larger predecessors, she was transported south to Santa Barbara for release. Less than a week later, she was caught in those same waters by a commercial fisherman, who called the phone number printed on her tag and reported she appeared to be in good health and looked as if she had recently fed. He then released her. Her tracking tag popped free in October 2008, still in waters near Santa Barbara.

The fifth shark was collected by aquarium staff near Malibu in August 2009 with the help of a spotter plane and a commercial fishing crew using a purse seine net. She, too, fed and swam well in the ocean pen before her transport to Monterey. She was healthy and feeding during her three months on exhibit, and was released into Monterey Bay in early November. The timing was prompted by the onset of aggressive behavior toward other sharks in the exhibit. Following release, she traveled south to Baja California, a distance of more than 500 miles. In March 2010, she was caught in a Mexican fisherman's gillnet and died – the only one of the five white sharks exhibited at the aquarium known to have died following a return to the wild.

The future: Field research continued in 2010, with no attempts to bring a sixth shark to Monterey because of the planned renovation of the million-gallon Open Sea exhibit. With the reopening of the exhibit in summer 2011, the tagging program and attempts to bring a shark to the aquarium will resume.

General White Shark Tagging Tracks Along the Eastern Pacific

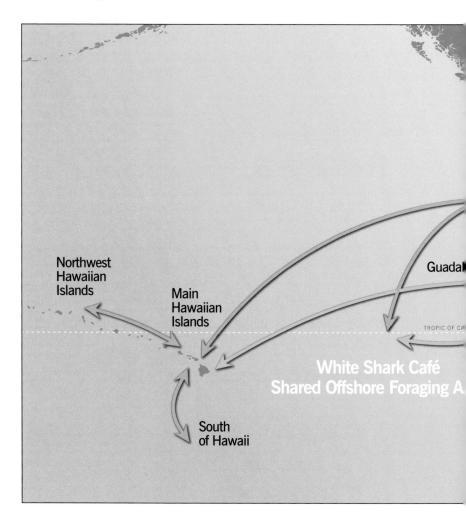

Northwest Hawaiian Islands

Main Hawaiian Islands

Guada

TROPIC OF CA

White Shark Café
Shared Offshore Foraging A

South of Hawaii

■ Adult White Sharks (Central California)
■ Adult White Sharks (Guadalupe Island, Mexico)
■ Juvenile White Sharks (Southern California Bight)
■ Juvenile White Sharks (released from Monterey Bay Aquarium)

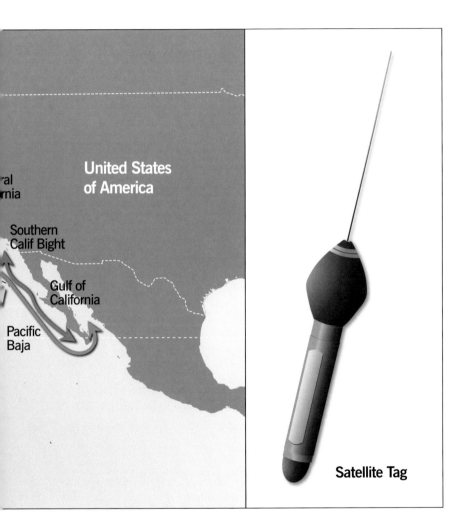

**United States
of America**

Southern
Calif Bight

Gulf of
California

Pacific
Baja

ral
rnia

Satellite Tag

A satellite tag, about the length of a dinner spoon, contains a tiny computer
that collects and stores data on temperature, depth and light (used to estimate
position). On a pre-programmed date, the tag pops off and floats to the surface,
where it transmits data to scientists via satellite. If the tag is recovered, even
more data are retrieved about the shark's travels.

Frontiers of Research

Great white sharks occupy a vital position at the top of the ocean's ecological food web. Yet they remain vulnerable to extinction and are protected under the Convention on International Trade in Endangered Species of Wild Fauna and Flora. Despite broad concern for their conservation, relatively little is known about their distribution and ecology – on the Pacific Coast and around the world. The aquarium's white shark research program, involving collaborators in the United States and Mexico, is making significant contributions to understanding great white shark populations in the Eastern Pacific, including where they travel, where they live and their basic physiology. The new data are generated from electronic tags, photo identification and genetic analyses using tissue and blood samples taken from each shark.

Collaborative research with Stanford University has revealed surprising facts about the lives of adult great white sharks, thanks to the use of 240 electronic tracking tags placed on 100 identified individual sharks at the Farallon Islands and at Point Año Nuevo since 2000. Many sharks have been tagged more than once, generating multiple years of information about their travels.

Data from the tags revealed that adult great white sharks — found seasonally along the California coast near seal and sea lion rookeries — migrate thousands of miles offshore to the Hawaiian Islands, and to a mid-ocean area halfway between Baja California and Hawaii dubbed by scientists as "The White Shark Café." Precisely why they visit these offshore waters remains a mystery, but when they return to the California coast they return consistently to the same local neighborhoods at the same time of year.

The research team has also learned that California's great white sharks comprise a genetically distinct population, long isolated from other great whites around the world. Knowing that the population is distinct allowed scientists to begin to census the population, and to monitor over time whether it's increasing or decreasing. As an isolated population, it can be more vulnerable since it won't be rescued or replenished via immigration from other populations.

The minimum population
in the central California
region is around 220 adult
and adolescent white sharks.

In the first-ever estimate of the central California population, scientists discovered it's surprisingly small. The minimum population in this region is around 220 adult and adolescent white sharks. The same electronic tags that afford unprecedented insights into the lives of adult great white sharks allow the white shark research team to map critical habitat used by young-of-the-year sharks. In collaboration with Stanford University, the University of Hawaii, Centro de Investigación Científica y de Educación Superior de Ensenada, Mexico (CICESE) and California State University, Long Beach, the team has placed electronic tags on 43 young sharks (through 2010) and documented a great white shark nursery area that extends from southern California through Baja California.

Sharks up to three years of age inhabit shallow coastal waters and frequently move back and forth between U.S. and Mexican territorial waters, the tags show. These findings indicate where young sharks are vulnerable (despite their protected status in both countries) to being caught as bycatch in coastal fisheries. The research underscores the need for international collaboration to create effective management plans for young great white sharks.

Having young white sharks on exhibit contributes in other ways to scientific understanding of the species. The aquarium team was able to accurately measure how much oxygen five sharks consumed during transport to Monterey – the first data ever collected on the metabolic rate of great white sharks.

By tracking how much food the sharks eat while on exhibit, and measuring their length and weight on arrival and at release, they gain insights into how much energy they need for swimming and life support, and how much is available for growth.

Other recent evidence gathered in the field by the white shark team suggests that young great whites are indeed being caught and sold commercially in Mexico. Over a three-year period, the research team and its partners found 40 mummified juvenile sharks in a desert dump site surrounding a fish camp in Baja California. Researchers are analyzing DNA from the teeth to help determine the population structure of great white sharks in California and Mexico. Eventually, the DNA results will contribute to a larger picture of overall genetic diversity and uniqueness of great white shark populations in the waters off California and Mexico.

Understanding and Protecting Sharks

Great white sharks are such magnificent creatures, and they've had an impact on our visitors like no other animals. It's clear from the looks on people's faces, the eagerness with which they seek them out, and their excitement when they see a white shark swimming on exhibit just a few feet away.

Each shark we've brought to Monterey has inspired awe and a sense of wonder – reaching millions of visitors. They have been powerful emissaries for ocean conservation, helping us raise awareness about the threats all sharks face around the world.

Equally important, our White Shark Research Project allows us to contribute significantly to scientific understanding of great white sharks.

We and our research partners are documenting the migrations of adult and juvenile white sharks in the Eastern Pacific, getting the first estimate of their numbers off the West Coast, and gaining new insights into their basic biological processes, such as how efficiently they convert food into body mass. All of what we've learned is new to science.

Understanding and protecting sharks is an urgent matter. Tens of millions are killed each year, accidentally in commercial fishing gear that targets other species, or deliberately for their fins. Healthy ocean ecosystems cannot survive without their top predators, including great white sharks. We must learn more about them, and inspire more people to care about their fate.

When you visit the aquarium, or purchase this book, or make a gift of support, you're helping further our work on behalf of great white sharks and a future with healthy oceans.

Many thanks,

Julie Packard

Julie Packard
Executive Director
Monterey Bay Aquarium

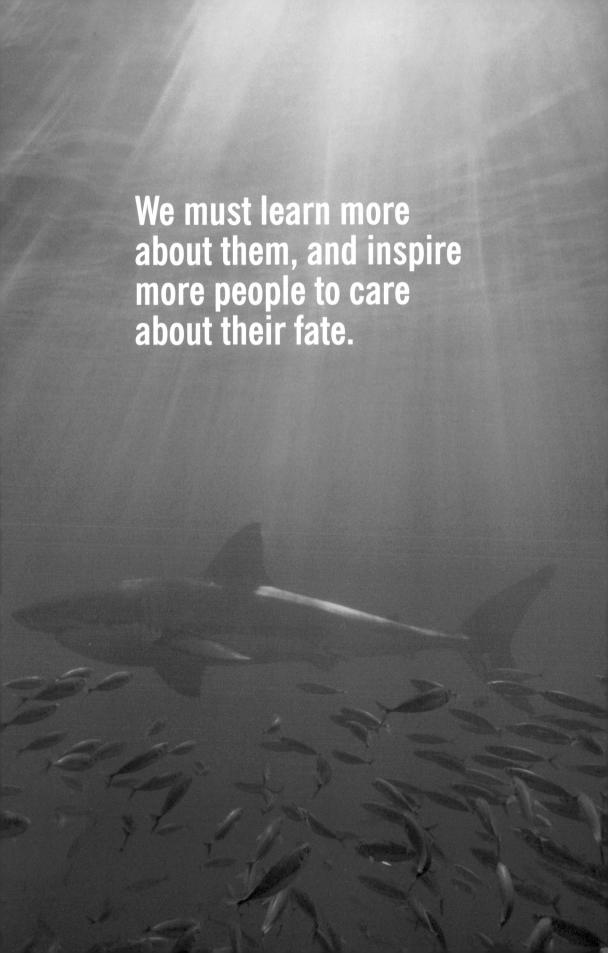

We must learn more about them, and inspire more people to care about their fate.

Learn More about Project White Shark

For more information plus videos, podcasts and the latest news about our White Shark Research Project, visit www.montereybayaquarium.org/cr/whiteshark.aspx.

Get the Latest White Shark News

Want to know when there's another great white shark on exhibit at the Monterey Bay Aquarium? Curious about what our researchers are learning in the field? Sign up to get e-mail alerts from www.montereybayaquarium.org.

Photography: Charles Arneson (Cover, 9), Brandon Cole (inside back cover), Angela Hains (13), Tom O'Neal (34), Mike Parry / Minden Pictures / National Geographic Stock (inside front cover, 32), Mike Parry / Minden Pictures (35),Tyson Rininger (6-7), Monterey Bay Aquarium (28-29), Kevin Weng (17), Randy Wilder (2, 4, 14-15, 18, 21, 23, 26, back cover), Chuck Winkler (11, 31)
Illustrations: Kirsten Carlson (24-25), reineckandreineck.com (28-29), Ann Caudle (36)
Writer: Ken Peterson, Project Manager: Karen Jeffries, Photo Research: Kris Ingram, Book Design: Jim Ales
Project Coordination – Service Systems Associates: Andrew Fischer, Barbara Reuther
ISBN: 978-1-878244-50-5
©2011 Monterey Bay Aquarium Foundation. All rights reserved. Printed in Canada on recycled paper.

MONTEREY BAY AQUARIUM
886 CANNERY ROW MONTEREY, CALIFORNIA 93940-1023
(831) 648-4888 WWW.MONTEREYBAYAQUARIUM.ORG